EGG to BUTTERFLY

Rachel Tonkin and Stephanie Fizer Coleman

WAYLAND
www.waylandbooks.co.uk

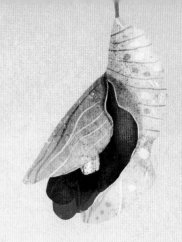

First published in Great Britain in 2019
by Wayland

Copyright © Hodder and Stoughton,
2019

Text first published in Looking at Lifecycles

Editor: Melanie Palmer
Designer: Lisa Peacock

HB ISBN: 978 1 5263 1021 7
PB ISBN: 978 1 5263 1022 4

Printed and bound in China

Wayland, an imprint of
Hachette Children's Group
Part of Hodder and Stoughton
Carmelite House
50 Victoria Embankment
London EC4Y 0DZ
An Hachette UK Company
www.hachette.co.uk
www.hachettechildrens.co.uk

MIX
Paper from
responsible sources
FSC® C104740

CONTENTS

Laying eggs

A butterfly is an insect.
An insect has six legs,
and antennae or feelers,
on its head. In spring,
a female butterfly lays
her eggs on leaves.

Inside the eggs

The butterfly's eggs stick to the leaves. Inside each egg a caterpillar is growing. It takes ten days for the caterpillar to grow.

New caterpillar

A caterpillar hatches from the egg. The caterpillar eats leaves to help it grow. It makes a leaf tent to shelter in. It uses special silk to stick the leaves together.

9

Shedding skin

After a few days
the caterpillar sheds its skin
so that it can grow bigger.
The caterpillar wraps
itself in leaves again
while it grows a new skin.

Fully grown

When a caterpillar is
fully grown, it gets ready
to turn itself into a butterfly.
It hangs from a leaf stem.

Pupa

The caterpillar sheds its skin
again to form a pupa.
This takes a few hours.
The pupa is covered in
a cocoon. This keeps it safe.

Changing

Inside the pupa, the caterpillar changes into a butterfly. After about three weeks the pupa splits open. A beautiful butterfly crawls out.

New butterfly

The new butterfly's
wings are wrinkled.
It climbs up the plant
to shake out its wings.
Then it flies away.

Flying away

In the autumn, some butterflies migrate. The butterflies fly to warmer countries. They come back in the spring in time to lay their eggs on leaves.

Butterfly life cycle

1 The female butterfly lays eggs.

2 The eggs stick to the leaves.

4 The caterpillar makes a leaf tent to shelter in.

3 A caterpillar hatches from an egg.

8 A new butterfly crawls out with wrinkled up wings.

9 The butterfly opens its wings and is ready to fly away.

6 Once it is fully grown the caterpillar forms a pupa.

5 The caterpillar sheds its skin so it can grow bigger.

7 After three weeks the pupa splits open.

23

Butterfly facts

The colour and shape of a butterfly's eggs are different for each type of butterfly.

Some butterflies only live for three days, others can live for six months.

Some butterflies can be as much as 30 cm wide.

Some butterflies fly thousands of kilometres when they migrate.

Butterflies taste with their feet. When they stand on food, they can taste it.

A butterfly's tongue is like a drinking straw so that it can sip nectar from flowers. When it is not feeding, the tongue curls up out of the way.

Butterflies' wings are covered with lots of tiny scales. This is what gives them their colour.

Butterfly quiz

Test your new knowledge with this butterfly life cycle quiz by answering the questions below.

Question 1
Where does the butterfly lay her eggs?

Question 2
How long does it take for a caterpillar to hatch out of its egg?

Question 3
How does the caterpillar make a shelter for itself?

Question 4
Why does a caterpillar shed its skin?

Question 5
What does the caterpillar do when it is ready to change into a butterfly?

Question 6
What happens next?

Question 7
What do some butterflies do in autumn?

ANSWERS ON PAGE 32

Make a colourful butterfly

What you will need:
- Sheet of white paper
- Pencil
- Scissors
- Paints and paintbrush
- Jar of clean water (to clean the paintbrush)

1. Fold the sheet of paper in half.

2. Copy this shape and cut it out.

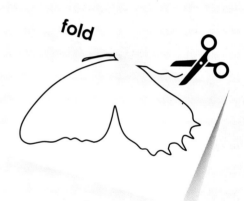

fold

3. Open up the paper butterfly and paint blobs of paint onto one wing.

4. Fold the other wing over to take a print of the paint blobs. Press down firmly.

5. Open the butterfly carefully and leave it to dry.

6. Notice that the patterns on the wings are symmetrical. That means they are the same on both sides of the butterfly's body.

Go on a butterfly hunt

What you will need:
- Notebook and pencil
- Field guide or identification sheet
- Bug viewer (optional)

This activity will work best in the spring or summer.

1. Take a notebook and pencil into your garden or local park on a sunny day. Record any butterflies you spot. Take an adult with you if you want to go on a butterfly hunt away from home.

2. Notice details about the butterfly. What colour is it? Does it have an unusual wing pattern? Which flower or plant was it resting or feeding on?

3. Ask an adult to help you download a spotter's guide from the Internet or borrow a field guide from the library. The Woodland Trust, Wildlife Trusts and other organisations have spotter sheets and online ID guides.

Plant a Butterfly Garden

What you will need:
- A spade
- A packet of wildflower seeds
- A patch of garden, a window box or large plant pot filled with garden compost
- A watering can

1. Ask an adult to help you clear a small patch of garden about 1 metre square. Clear it of plants, weeds or grass. Or you can use a window box or plant pot and fill it with soil.

2. Sow the wildflower seeds, following the instructions on the packet.

3. Water the seeds once a week if it does not rain.

4. When the wildflowers are in flower, spend time watching butterflies and other insects visit your flowers.

Butterfly words

Antennae
The feelers on the head of an insect. They are used for smelling.

Caterpillar
The stage in the life of a butterfly between hatching from an egg and forming a pupa.

Cocoon
The covering of the pupa. It protects the caterpillar inside.

Insect
An animal with six legs and two antennae. The body of an insect is divided into three parts.

Leaf tent
Some caterpillars make a tent from folded leaves to protect them while they grow.

Migrate
To fly from one place to another at regular times of the year.

Pupa
The stage in the life of a butterfly between being a caterpillar and becoming an adult butterfly.

Index

QUIZ ANSWERS: 1 On a leaf; **2** About ten days (it depends on the butterfly – some eggs take a longer or shorter time to hatch); **3** It sticks two leaves together using silk threads; **4** It sheds its skin to grow bigger; **5** It makes a pupa or chrysalis around itself; **6** A butterfly crawls out of the pupa; **7** They migrate.